Call to Awaken the Laity **Leadership Training 2**

Church and Laity

Call to Awaken the Laity **Leadership Training**

Vol 2 Church and Laity

Copyright©2005 by John H. Oak

Published by DMI Press
1443-26 Seocho-1dong, Seocho-ku, Seoul 137-865, Korea

All rights reserved. No part of this book may be reproduced in any manner whatsoever without prior written permission from the publisher, except where noted in the text and in the case of brief quotations embodied in critical articles and reviews.

First Printing, April 2005
Printed in Seoul, Korea

ISBN 89-5731-069-X 03230

Visit our Web Site : www.discipleN.com

Call to Awaken the Laity **Leadership Training 2**

Church and Laity

John H. Oak

DMI

What is Leadership Training?

Korean churches have been very passive in equipping the lay Christians to minister God's Word to other Christians. The main role of the laity was to teach in the Sunday schools or to participate in traditional worship oriented small group.

The laity lacked biblical training in their churches. Typically, people were immediately asked to serve if they appeared to have some faith or talents. This has caused many problems within the church and a majority of lay people are experiencing difficulty in maintaining their spiritual fervor.

Leadership Training prepares those who have gone completed the discipleship training and have shown the ability to serve others by teaching the Word. The focus of discipleship training was to guide the believers to be like Jesus and to live like Him. The emphasis of leadership Training is to guide them to become lay minister to teach others under pastoral supervision. This is very important and significant because we are searching for potential lay leaders who can be assist the pastor side by side in discipling the laity to be Christlike.

It is preferred that those who have completed the discipleship training engage themselves in the teaching ministry, but that is not always the case. Therefore, it is important to discover what your gift is and where you would like to serve after you have completed the discipleship training. If you do not have the gift of teaching, then you should not consider the leadership Training, but devote yourself in the area that best fits your gift.

Teaching ministry is one of the most important elements of the church. Church is the body of Christ that needs various talents. However, teaching ministry is not better or superior to other ministries. Nevertheless it is foundational and requires more preparation and training than any other ministries.

Therefore, serious responsibility comes with the teaching ministry. Misinterpretation of the scripture and false teaching can cause fatal damages within the community. On the other hand, when it is done right with the right mind and heart, you will experience abundant fruits. That is because lives are being renewed, and transformed by God's Word and what can be more exciting than witnessing a transforming life in Christ.

If you are called to teaching ministry, you should be praising and thanking God, for entrusting you with this incredible ministry under your care. During training, you must prayerfully desire for a greater development of your gift in teaching. At the same time, seek for a greater empowerment of the Holy Spirit. You must have a heart burning with passion for even one soul and as wide as an ocean to be able to accept anyone. You must bring yourself to complete obedience as Paul did, so that you may lack nothing as you become more like Jesus Christ in your character and life. I pray that you will envision what Isaiah once had seen in a dream.

"Then will all your people be righteous and they will possess the land forever. They are the shoot I have planted, the work of my hands, for the display of my splendor. The least of you will become a thousand, the smallest a mighty nation. I am the Lord; in its time I will do this swiftly."

(Isaiah 60:21~22)

Points to Consider

The following points should be kept in order to complete the leadership Training successfully.

1. In order to benefit fully from the training, you should love and trust your leader and pray for him faithfully.

2. Go to every meeting and complete the training. Members might face one or two crisis during the training, but every member should help and care for each other to overcome the crisis.

3. Prepare for each lesson. Your preparation makes a big difference to your training.

4. Do the weekly homework. Develop from the beginning a habit of doing your homework thoroughly and regularly.

5. This is an opportunity to train the whole person. A person who only uses his or her head might well become a cold theoretician, but cannot become a disciple who loves Jesus. Our mind, emotion, and will must be involved in order to experience the wonderful intervention of the

Holy Spirit. Have you learned the Word? Then embrace the Word and pray. Prayer is putting what you have learned into your heart. Then immediately apply the Word to your daily life. You will discover that you are becoming more like Christ as you learn, understand, and put the Word into practice. "Oh, how I love your law! I meditate on it all day long" (Psalms 119:97).

6. You must continually sharpen your teaching skills. Also, carefully observe other leader who are already in teaching ministry, analyze their strengths and weaknesses.

7. You will experience tremendous blessing when you begin to lead & train your own family with biblical truths.

8. You must remember that you must become a prayer warrior. There is no shortcut to this. Prayer will enable you to become a cloud that brings showers of blessings.

Contents

Table of Contents

Appendix

Church and Laity

This volume focuses on changing the perception of our self image and of the church. After our conversion, it is important to learn and understand the relationship between church and the laity. Healthy understanding of self image will lead into a proper understanding of the doctrine of church. Your perception toward church will heavily depend on how you perceive yourselves as member of that church.

1
What is Church?

During Jesus' earthly ministry, he trained His disciples and sent the Holy Spirit after his ascension. This was to receive glory and worship from God's people who were to be saved through the church. Therefore, the church is the place where the risen Christ reveals His will and God is truly worshiped and praised. Hence, the church must always be ready to establish God's will by executing His purpose toward the present generation.

Nowadays, there are many service attenders but are clueless of what church is about. If we have a proper understanding of the church, then we will be able to live a consistent Christian life.

A skewd understanding of church is derived from unhealthy spiritual life. We can lose our saltiness and become self centered. Healthy doctrine of church is a must to the laymen. Only those who have a proper understanding of the church can be used effectively by God's hand. Ask yourself, what is my definition of the church?

Note

1. Examine and see what the following Scriptures say about the church.

- I Corinthians 1:2

1) What are the two expressions of the church found in this verse?

- sanctified in Christ Jesus
- called to be saints

2) What does "those sanctified" mean?

Jesus had sanctified us through his death and resurrection.

3) What is the correct definition of the church; people, building or organization?

the church is the ppl who God has called.

Note

- Ephesians 2:19

1) Why is church called God's family?

We are members in his household.

2) Discuss similar characteristics between church and family.

We do everything together; go through trials and joys together. We are inseparable, one in Christ (like family will always be family).

2. The church is the gathering of God's people who are called out of the world. How does Jesus' parable in Matthew 22:1~14 illustrate this truth?

1) Summarize the text.

A King gave a wedding feast for his son. He told his servants to bring the invitees, but the guests wouldn't come. They treated the servants badly then killed them. The King got angry and with his troops killed the ppl and burned their city. The King sent his servants to find any guests they could find on the streets, so the banquet was filled with guests.

Note

2) How were they invited to the wedding banquet and what was the reason?

The latter guests were just invited because former guests wouldn't go.

3) How do the following words reveal the characteristics of church?

- King

God is the King. He is controlling and ruling. We the church are his ppl.

- Servants

The servants do the King's will. Whatever God the King wants, servants (laity) are the ones who carry it out.

- Invitation

God invites anyone to come to the wedding feast of his Son, his servants go out to bring guests.

Note

- Banquet

Heaven. Entering into God's kingdom

- Wedding clothes

Jesus' righteousness that covers us. God providing the "clothes" for us.

4) How should you respond when you know that you have been called to this banquet?

Thankful, joyful, honored, humbled

3. The church is the body of Christ's disciples who are sent into the world. Explain this truth with the following Scriptures.

- John 20:21 "Peace be with you. As the Father has sent me, even so I am sending you."

1) Describe the background of the text.

The disciples were together when the Resurrected Jesus came to them.

Note

2) Who is "you" referring to?

the disciples

3) Clarify the meaning of "sending."

~~G~~ Jesus ~~is sending his disciples~~ will use his disciples to spread the gospel.

- Matthew 28:18~20

1) What is the background of the text?

Right before Jesus ascension. His last words.

2) What is Jesus' commandment here?

Go and make disciples of everyone, baptizing them in the name of the Father, Son, Holy Spirit.

3) Who is "you" referring to?

the disciples. Anyone who carries out the command.

Note

4) Why is Jesus' command absolute?

He has all authority in heaven and earth and he said he would always be with us. He already has demonstrated his love on cross and as he said he would, came to life again.

5) Are you accountable to the command?

Yes.

4. The following two verses give evidence that church is the body of disciples who are sent into the world.

- Ephesians 2:20

1) Paraphrase the text.

Jesus is our cornestone. Stable. Critical part that building is ↑ and square. Church is built on foundations of apostles and prophets. We are here because the ppl before us obeyed God and ~~w~~ spread the gospel.

2) Who is "you" that is built on the foundation?

the Church, [us. Ppl now] applies to us. the Ephesian church.

Note

3) Who are the 'apostles' and 'prophets' referring to?

servants of God. the
12 disciples. Prophets of old/new

4) Listen to your leader's lecture.

- Acts 1:8

1) Rewrite the text in your own words.

You, disciples, will receive power
when the Holy Spirit comes
upon you. to be the witnesses
to the ends of the earth.

2) Listen to your leader's lecture on the purpose of the coming of the Holy Spirit.

Note

3) You are called to be sent into the World. Explain this in relation to the Holy Spirit?

Holy Spirit is with us and empowers us to be witnesses for Christ

5. Church can be defined as follow: "The Church is God's people called out of the world and Christ's disciples who are sent into the world." Discuss the following questions.

1) Are churches today more focused on gathering His people or delegating them as disciples of Christ? Why?

2) What are some spiritual symptoms when a Christian ignores the great commission?

selfish. Forgetful about his return. Mundane life.

6. Write down what you have learned about the church.

The church is the ppl God sent into the world to be his witnesses, and to gather them into the Kingdom.

2

Purpose of Church: Worship

Christians must constantly remind themselves why church exists in this world. A church that constantly addresses this question is likely to stay on course because it will not lose sight of its purpose and vision. The existence of church can be defined in the following statement, "The Church exists in this world for the glory of God." However, this statement is too abstract. It needs further explanation.

The purpose of church can be defined in three aspects; worship, training, witnessing.

Note

1. The first purpose of the church in the world is for God Himself. Read Isaiah 43.

1) Summarize verse 7.

Everyone called by God's name was created for his glory who he formed and made

2) Who is "you" in, "I have called you by name" in verse 1?

"you" is Israel.

3) Why did God create them?

He created them for him.

4) Simplify verse 21 in your own words.

God created us to praise his name.

Note

5) What does it mean to praise God? Consider the following text. (Revelation 15:3~4; Psalm 40:5, 16)

singing, worship, fearing / glorifying God's name. Tell of God's deeds. Rejoice and be glad in Him. praise his name.

6) What is the purpose of the church that you can discover here?

We are to speak of the things God has done. We are to sing and praise His name.

2. What is the most fundamental thing the church should do for the glory of God? Read John 4:23~24.

in our spirit heart not flesh

1) Simplify the text in your own words.

Worship God in Spirit and truth.
Word

2) How do you give true worship?

sing, meditate, thank God

Note

3) Our worship needs to be alive. Write down the most inspiring and moving aspect of service at your church.

praise
sermon

4) How committed are you to Sunday worship?

I'm committed.

5) Are you content with your worship service? Why not? After listening to your leader, evaluate the reason you have written down.

3. Worshipping God does not end with the public worship at church. What does Romans 12:1 teach concerning this matter?

Note

1) Reiterate the text.

In view of God's mercy, give our life (bodies) as an offering to God, it's holy and pleasing and our act of worship.

2) What is the "spiritual worship" we ought to offer?

Our lives (bodies) surrendered to God as a sacrifice

3) What is "offering of your bodies" alluding to?

Our lives

4) Are you convinced that your whole life represents an act of holy worship? What do you do differently from others because of this conviction?

No. I want it to be though.

Note

5) Do you believe that what you do is an act of worship to God, whether it is significant or insignificant? How are you serving Christ through your life? Evaluate your roles in your family and church.

I'm serving Christ by being a good wife. When I share the good news, I am serving Christ.

6) Why do you feel hopeless and spirithally depressed in your work place or home at times?

it may be because I am not sharing Christ.

4. If there is one thing that the children of God are not ashamed of, it is worship. Worship is both a privilege and blessing. Living a worshipful life is the essence of Christian life. We must try to live a holistic life by exhibiting God's truths and characters in all we do. What will the worldly people learn when they see the children of God, who are truly living a life of worship?

They'll see that God is alive.

Note

5. Examine and see if you had learned anything new about worship. Write down if there are things that the Holy Spirit is convicting you now. Also write how you can become a better, joyful worshipper.

I have to continue to be changed. I need to surrender and speak more about Christ. Actively live and speak about Jesus.

3

Purpose of Church: Training

Now we will study the second purpose of church. A church must properly function to remain healthy. Finding a good church is as important as finding your soul mate. If a church does not guide or care its congregation with firm biblical teaching, then nobody would be able to maintain their faith to the end, or withstand the temptations from the Devil.

In this sense, church is a spiritual mother to the believers. Just as it is hard to imagine a baby without a mother, so is a person without a church. Nevertheless, the church does not only exist to safeguard the sheep, but also to train the laymen in the Word of God. They are to be strong in their faith so that they may serve one another in the body, and become the light and the salt of the world. Church has been entrusted to teach the Word.

If the church does not exist, where would people go to learn and receive the spiritual training?

Note

Sardis
twice captured in history. Watchmen neglected duty.

1. The second purpose of church is to maintain its health and growth of the body. Study the church in Sardis.

1) Reiterate Revelation 3:1~3 in your own words.

I know your works. You are known to be alive, but you're dead. Wake up and strengthen what is left. I haven't found your works complete in the sight of my God. Repent and keep what you heard.

2) The church in Sardis is gravely ill. How can you tell?

They are dead.
Jesus tells them to wake up.

Acts 14:26
commended to the grace of God for the work that they had fulfilled.

3) What does "I have not found your deeds complete" mean?

wants them
God ~~gave th~~ to carry out his will, but they aren't doing it. Perhaps the commands God has already given us, Go and make disciples... love the Lord your God.

4) What are symptoms of unhealthy church?

dead (asleep)
incomplete work
Impenitent
Not watchful
Not remembering and keep what was received and heard

Note

5) From verse 3, why did the church in Sardis experience hardship?

They were forgetful of what they received and heard. Didn't keep it and no repentance.

6) Could your church be experiencing a similar spiritual illness?

I don't think so. I would hope not. We are awake.

2. What command did Jesus give to the church before His ascension? Consider Matthew 28:18~20.

1) Summarize Jesus' command by using five verbs that appear in verses 19~20.

Go, make, baptize, teach, observe

Note

2) Training is enabling someone to learn and live by that principle or instruction. What is the difference between instructing and training? Give example.

Instructing is just teaching, like with words. Training is showing and putting disciples in place. Teachers instruct. When Training with trainers, they motivate and push you and are alongside with you to get you to your goal.

3) Does your current training relate to Jesus' commandment?

Yes

3. If a church is faithful to the Word, what benefits will it reap? Look up the following references.

- 1 Peter 2:2

Will grow up into salvation The Word in us will sanctify us and in the end save us.

Note

- Acts 20:32

build person up and give them inheritance

- 1 Thessalonians 5:14 (cf 1Thess 3:11)

'word will lead

We can admonish the idle, encourage the fainthearted, help the weak

- Acts 19:8~10, 18~20

will speak boldly, reasoning, and persuading about kingdom of God. People will hear God's word. Going out to speak of Christ.

4. What did Jesus Christ bestow upon the church in order to train the people?

Note

- Ephesians 4:11~13

1) Rephrase the text in your own words.

He gave apostle, prophets, evangelists, shepherds, teachers to train the believers for work of ministry, for building up the body until everyone attains faith/knowledge of God to mature manhood, becoming more like Christ

2) What kinds of roles has the Lord sanctioned for the church?

- to train
- buildup
- teach
- help grow/mature

3) Define the three roles of a pastor.

to equip
to build up
to help mature

4) Are you receiving guidance from your pastor to apply his teachings to daily life?

yes

Note

5) Did you receive any formal training before of after you began to serve in your church? What are the advantages or disadvantages, before and after?

No formal training beforehand. Disadv is that you don't know what you're doing because you're just thrown in.

• 2 Timothy 3:16, 17

1) Rephrase the text in your own words.

All of the bible is from God and is useful for teaching, rebuking, correcting, and training to be holy so that the man of God may be complete, ready for every good work.

2) Why did God give us the Bible? (v. 17)

We will be complete, ready for every good work.

Note

3) The bible teaches that the church must have the Word of God as well as the pastor. Why is it important to have them both?

The church needs it themselves
The Pastor cannot live
your life for you but with
God's word, church must
shine.

4) Examine the four functions of the Bible and discuss its implications. (v. 16)

Teach - bible is meant to be
taught. What is in the Word
is what ppl need. They do not have
the knowledge, they must be taught.
Rebuke - God's word steers
us to the right pl.
Train - helps us grow, keeps us accountable

5) How are you being taught, rebuked, corrected and trained by the teachings of the Bible so that you may live a life of integrity and character?

God's word is training me to be
watchful. As I read, im reminded
that this is the truth and
the greater reality we live
for.

Note

6) Reflect with a prayerful heart how much change has taken place in your character and life after your commitment to the Discipleship and Leadership Training.

4

Purpose of Church: Witnessing

The final purpose of the church is to witness to the world. A church must continuously build up disciples to be sent into the world to share and live out the gospel. Wherever they go, they must edify the church through their exemplary lives. Churches must be the light and hope to the world. Sadly, we see that the world has a low view on the church.

Church must not remain merely as a small mustard seed, but grow into a tree and proclaim the message and purpose of God.

Note

Hallow: make holy or sacred

1. What is the task of the church today?

- Matthew 6:9~10

1) Paraphrase the text in your own words.

Pray like this:
Our Father in heaven, Holy is your name. Your kingdom come your will be done on earth like it's done in heaven

2) Explain the three parts of prayer and its significance.

1- Make holy/sacred God's name.
2- God's kingdom continue to advance
3- God's will be done

3) For this prayer to be answered, gospel must be preached to all nations. Why?

He desires all men to be saved.

Note

2. The church must proclaim the gospel to the world. What does the Bible say about this?

- Matthew 28:19~20 Go and make disc of all nations
- Mark 16:15 Go into world and proclaim Gospel to whole creation
- Luke 24:47~48 repentance and forgiveness of sins should be proclaimed in his name to all nations

1) What is common in all three texts?

Gospel to all nations

2) What does it mean to preach the good news 'to all creation' or 'to all nations'? Does it mean to preach the good news to every person or to the public in general so they can hear? (Acts 13:48; Romans 15:19, 23)

To the public

Note

- Acts 1:8

1) This verse teaches that we must all be witnesses to the gospel. Why?

Holy Spirit will come upon us to preach to ends of the earth

2) How does this verse allude to the development of the world mission?

To the ends of the earth

3) Where is your 'Jerusalem' and 'ends of the earth'?

home,
Church.
School.
Where I am

Note

4) Jesus doesn't want the gospel to be proclaimed only in Jerusalem. Why not?

He wants whole world ~~to~~ know

5) How passionate are you in sharing the gospel or going on mission trips inland and abroad?

I've been on hold due to school and financial reasons. I expect to go after I graduate

3. Consider the following table. When do you think the world will be fully evangelized? What must the church do to accomplish this task?

Population by religion (Unit : million)

Religion / Year	1900	1970	2001
World Population	1,619.8	3701.9	6128.5
Christian Population	558	1222.5	2024.9
Christian Population Ratio	34.4	33	33
Unreached Group	813.2	1634.8	1637.5
Unreached Group Ratio	50.2	44.2	26.7
Islam	200.1	553.5	1213.4
Hinduism	203	462.6	823.8
Buddhism	127.1	233.4	363.7

(Berrett & Johnson, 2001)

Note

Missionary & Mission Organization

	1900	1970	2001
Number of Foreign Missionary	62,000	240,000	425,000
Number of Mission organization	600	2,200	4,100

(Berrett & Johnson, 2001)

Bible Translation

In Progress: 1500 + languages	Partly Done: 902 languages
New Testament only: 960 languages	Entire Bible: 371 languages
To be translated: 3000 + languages	

(Global Bible Translators, 1999)

4. Answer the following questions.

1) Are you aware of 10/40 window?

Yes

Note

2) Which mission organization are you most familiar with?

NMMC. Not really any outside my church.

3) Are you supporting any missionaries? (prayer/financial support)

Yes. Joe / Joyce

4) If opportunity rises, would you like to commit yourself as professional missionary in the future?

Yes

Dear friends, I urge you, as aliens and strangers in ~~this~~ the world, to abstain from sinful desires, which war against your soul. Live such good lives among the pagans that, though they accuse you of doing wrong, they may see your good deeds and glorify God on the day he visits us.

1 Pe 2:11-12

5

Qualification of a Disciple: Total Dependence

The word *disciple* appears more than 250 times in the Gospels and Acts. The word is referred to those who believed and followed Christ.

When the early church emerged in Jerusalem, all believers were called disciples. They followed, learned and obeyed His teachings. They were like Jesus and lived like Jesus. They were even prepared to die for Jesus. Jesus commanded us to make disciples of all nations.

Anyone who wants to live a Christ centered life must be equipped with three things. First, he must totally depend on Jesus. Second, he must witness Christ both in his words and action wherever he goes. Third, he must be a servant. Let's study what it means to be totally dependent on Christ.

Note

1. Find out what kind of person was called disciple in the New Testament.

given authority

- Matthew 10:1

authority given to drive out demons · evil spirits and heal every disease and sickness

Know the truth

- John 8:31

Know the truth and the truth will set you free

was baptized

- Acts 2:41

Baptized

2. From Luke 14:25~33, discuss the cost of following Jesus.

1) Paraphrase the text in your own words.

Must love Jesus before parents, wife, children, brothers, sisters, even my own life. We have to carry our own cross and follow Him.

Note

2) Observe how Jesus distinguishes the disciples from the crowd who followed Him. What can you learn from this?

distinction b/w ~~cross~~ following Christ and not are clear

3) Why does He distinguish between the two?

to explain what it means to follow Him.

4) What is the first cost that must be paid to be his disciple? Why?

Hate everyone else including self.

5) Is he saying to disown your family?

NO, but yes. Yes because we must put Jesus first. He is before our families. His will supercedes our will and our families.

Note

6) If you truly love Jesus you will be able to truly love your family and neighbors. How is this true?

Yes because as we experience God's love, His love in us will enable us to love others.

Our experience of God's mercy and love will lead us to do the same to others.

7) What is the second cost that must be paid to be his disciple? (v. 27)

Carry own cross and follow Him

8) List all the crosses you ought to bear in order to follow Jesus.

Family - loving them and praying for them
Classmates
Church

The ppl God places in our lives.

9) What is the third cost you must pay? (v. 33)

Give up everything He has

Note

10) What does it mean to give up everything? (Matthew 6:24)

NOT serving two masters. Hate one and love the other. Devoted to one and despise the other. Cant serve Money and God.

11) Have you surrendered everything before Jesus?

I don't think so. I feel I have a lot of my will that I have

12) What does the parable of the tower and the negotiations teach?

Count the cost. Thinking through before committing. Do not take following Jesus lightly.

13) You cannot be Jesus' disciple unless you are ready to pay the costs mentioned above. Does this mean then you cannot be saved?

No, we can be saved, but this has to happen. It may not be now but the surrender must happen.

Note

3. There is a lesson we can learn from those who failed to follow Jesus. Review Luke 9:57~62.

1) Paraphrase the text.

Son of Man has no place to lay his head. Dead bury dead, but you go and proclaim kingdom of God. No one who puts his hand to the plow and looks back is fit for the kingdom of heaven

2) Did the first person succeed or fail in his attempt to follow Jesus? Why?

No. He said he will follow Jesus wherever He goes.

3) If he failed what was the reason behind it?

He wanted a home, comfort

4) Can you see yourself in him?

Yes

Note

5) Why couldn't the second person follow Jesus?

He wanted to first bury his father.

6) Does this mean you can't even attend your parent's funeral?

Some ways yes. Jesus comes first. Proclaiming the kingdom takes precedence

7) Are you living a Christian life with right priorities?

I've gotten so selfish. I have to give up everything if I want to be a disciple

8) The third person took initiative and decided to follow Jesus, but what was the problem in Jesus' eyes?

he was putting his hand to the plow and looking back

Note

9) Share your similar example analogous to this person.

10) Reflect and see if you have a similar problem.

4. Define 'total dependence' in your own term. Are you totally dependant upon Jesus? Why not?

Total dependence is following Christ with your whole heart. His will becomes your will. My will dies.

14: Lk 26-27, 33

If anyone comes to me and does not hate his father and mother, his wife and children, his brothers and sisters - yes, even his own life - he cannot be my disciple. And anyone who does not carry his cross and follow me cannot be my disciple. In the same way, any of you who does not give up everything he has cannot be my disciple.

Lk 24:46-48
He told them, "This is what is written: The Christ will suffer and rise from the dead on the third day and repentance and forgiveness of sins will be preached in his name to all nations, beginning at Jesusalem. You are witnesses of these things.

6

Qualification of a Disciple: Witness

Bible shows that the ultimate task of a disciple is to testify and witness Him. Therefore it is inevitable for a disciple to consider this as his calling. His words need to be consistent with his action. It will be contradicting if he lives a double standard life style.
However, one thing that must be kept in mind is that no matter how commendable the action is, it is incomplete without the Word. This explains why Jesus' disciples shared the testimony of the Word before their life changing testimony. The gospel is transmitted through God's Word. The power of salvation is manifested when the Word is proclaimed. Paul's questions, "And how can they hear without someone preaching to them? And how can they preach unless they are sent?" show explicitly how important proclaiming the Word is to Christians.

Note

1. Read Luke 24:45~49. What is the ultimate purpose of being Jesus' disciples?

1) Paraphrase the text in your own words.

Jesus opened their minds so they could understand. Jesus will suffer and rise from the dead on the third day. Repentance and forgiveness of sin will be preached in his name to all nations, starting at Jerusalem. Disciples are witnesses

2) What was Jesus' final appeal to the disciples? (v. 48)

"You are witnesses of these things."

3) What did He ask of them to testify? (vv. 46~47)

Tell them what Jesus did. He died and rose again for ppl to repent and their sins to be forgiven. Tell them the gospel & What is written.

4) Why do you think Jesus asked them to be His witnesses and what does this imply?

because they are Jesus' witnesses. They lived w/Him and walked w/Him. This implies that it applies to us.

Note

5) What are the three criteria of discipleship? See vv. 45, 48~49 & John 20:21.

① Jesus must open their minds.

② Filled w/ Holy Spirit

③ Sent by Jesus.

2. Based on Acts 2, what is the purpose of the coming of the Holy Spirit?

- Verse 4

They were filled and began speaking in tongues.

- Verse 11

disciples were declaring wonders of God in other tongues.

- Verse 36

testify Christ.

Note

- 4:20

can't help speaking about what we saw / heard.

3. Do all believers have to be witnesses or is it only for a few who are called to this task? (Act 1:8) All

1) Explain how all Christian ought to be witnesses of Jesus. (v. 8; 2:17)

will be filled w/ Holy Spirit, for sons / daughters to prophecy, young men will see visions, old men will dream dreams

2) Are you convinced that you are a witness because you are filled with the Holy Spirit?

Yes.

Note

3) Do you believe that witnessing is a spiritual gift? If so, have you used this as an excuse for not witnessing because you thought you are not gifted in this area?

No its not a gift but every believer must witness.

4. Read Acts 4:23~31 and see what we can learn from the early church.

1) Summarize the text.

Peter and John were questioned. When they were released, they praised God and prayed. The place they were meeting was shaken and they were all filled w/the Holy Spirit and spoke God's Word boldly.

2) How did they overcome their persecution in their prayers?

They were filled with the Holy Spirit.

Note

3) What was the main concern of their prayer?

They asked God to enable them to speak w/great boldness.

4) Find any evidence that shows God was indeed pleased with their prayer.

He shook the place where they stood and filled them w/the Holy Spirit

5) Do you wish to experience the empowering of the Holy Spirit in your prayer?

Yes!

7

Qualification of a Disciple: Servant

Disciple of Jesus must be a servant. Jesus Himself lived a life of servanthood. A disciple must follow His master because he is to make Him known through his life. Therefore, living like Jesus becomes an inseparable principle.

Disciple must love his neighbors as himself and that love must be characterized by joyful giving and serving. A disciple who only gives lip service and refuses self sacrifice is not worthy in the kingdom of God. How could a disciple, who disregards serving, be able to inherit the kingdom of God?

Note

1. Read John 13:13~17 and explain why Jesus' disciple must be a servant.

1) Paraphrase the text in your own words.

You call me "Lord" and "Teacher" and that is right because it's who I am.
I washed your feet so you shou wash one another's feet. I've set an example for you to follow.
I tell you the truth, servant can't be greater than master.
You will be blessed if you do them.

2) What does Jesus want to communicate through the text?

He is Lord and Teacher. He washed our feet, so we are to do what He did. We the servants aren't better (above) than our master, so just as He set an example for us, we are to follow what He did.

3) Describe Jesus' intention of brining up the subject of servanthood at that moment.

This is before Jesus is about to go to the cross. He wants to do/say/leave to them the most important thing, so what Jesus brought up at this time is very significant.

Note

4) Disciple of Jesus is destined to serve others. Why?

(vv. 13~14)

because Jesus Himself served.
Jesus our Teacher and
Lord washed our feet
and He told us, His disciples,
to do the same to others.

5) Have you ever washed someone's feet? Describe

how you felt at that moment.

yes. I remember thinking,
Lord be glorified.
I remembered also that
Jesus did the same for
me. He washed all my filth
and sins. And I'm
doing now is what Jesus told me to do.

6) What is the pronoun "these" in verse 17 referring to?

And why is it a basis for blessing?

Footwashing. Act of serving
as Jesus served. because
we are obeying Christ
and to give is better than
receiving.

Note

7) How are you trying to imitate and follow Jesus' teachings in your life? Give specific examples.

Love others by helping them w/rides.

2. What position did Apostle Paul take when serving the church?

- Philippians 1:1

servants of Christ Jesus.

- 2 Corinthians 4:5

1) Paraphrase the text in your own words.

We don't preach ourselves, but Jesus christ as Lord and your servants for Jesus' sake.

2) Why did Paul consider himself as servant?

He does what Jesus says to do. Jesus is the Master, who has the authority and is the one who tells Paul what to do. Paul's life is not his own.

Note

3) However, there are instances where ministers use this verse to their advantage. Discuss.

like I am a servant of Christ, so you must listen to me and serve me. Perhaps instead of serving like Christ, they expect to be served.

4) What does it mean for a minister to be a servant of believers?

it's to do what Jesus did. It's following Jesus examples.

5) How would laymen respond when ministers serve with such humility and servanthood?

They would in turn do the same.

Note

3. Jesus' disciple should live a life of servanthood with two motives in mind.

1) The first motive (I John 3:16)

Since Jesus ~~s~~ laid down his life for us, we should for one another.

2) The second motive (Exodus 21:1~6)

Love.

3) What is your motive of serving?

Jesus saved me and died for me, I want to serve others as He did for me. I am a totally depraved nobody but he loved me and died for me. I want to live to help others know the love of Christ.

Note

4. Answer the next questions after reading Matthew 25:31~46.

1) Summarize the text.

Jesus will come back in glory and separate sheep / goats. Sheeps who lived a life of love/service, God will give kingdom. Goats who didn't will go where there is gnashing of teeth. (eternal punishment)

2) What is the difference between the sheep's and the goat's reply?

(They both didnt know that what was being done was to Christ.) One group showed love to others and the other didnt.

3) What can you learn from their replies?

What we do for others is being done to Christ. What we do or not.

4) What can you learn from the sheep and the goat?

We must live a life of love and servanthood.

We must live it!

8

Members of the Body and the Cooperative Ministry

Having a proper understanding of the church is vital in order to serve the church effectively. Otherwise the church can become dry and institutional. The church is the body of Christ. Apostle Paul intentionally compares the church to a physical body. Just like the body needs the right nutrition to grow and be healthy, so does the church. Every church member must remember that each one of them are an important part of the church body, not just Sunday service attender.

Note

1. Explain the relationships among Jesus Christ, the church and the believers?

- 1 Corinthians 12:27

- Colossians 1:18

2. The Holy Spirit bestows His gifts on the church accordingly. How does I Corinthians 12:27~31 illustrate this truth.

1) Paraphrase the text.

Note

2) How do you define 'gifts'?

3) These eight gifts are selected among the many. They can be divided into two categories; ones that are identified as church office and the ones that are not. List them.

4) What is your gift and how did you find out about it?

Note

5) Do you select your own gift or is it given to you by the Holy Spirit? Give your reason.

6) What does it mean that you can desire a better gift?

7) How can you desire a better gift? (12:31; 14:1)

3. Review the relationship of the members of the church in I Corinthians 12:14~26.

Note

1) Verses 14~20 expound on the diversity of the members. What does this parable teach about diffferent gifts?

2) Verses 21~24 describe that in essence, all members are equal. How can this be understood with regard to the different gift that each member possess?

3) Verses 24~26 show the genuine care and cooperative ministry among the members. What are some of the benefits/outcomes of such community? (v. 26)

Note

4) Are there people in your church whom you can share your laughter and tears sincerely?

5. Examine Colossians 3:16~17 and see what happens when everyone encourages one another with God's Word.

1) Paraphrase the text.

2) Who is "you"? (1:2)

Note

3) Who can teach each other?

4) List two blessings when we build each other with God's Word? (vv. 16~17)

5) When you complete this training, you will be ready to teach and admonish as lay minister. Are you ready?

Note

Doctrinal Summary

_ The church is the body of Christ and the believers are its members.

_ There are no comparative merits among the members. All members are equal.

_ Each member has his/her own unique gifts.

_ The Holy Spirit bestows gifts on the body of the church.

_ All gifts are different but have same purpose which is to serve one another.

_ It is sinful to use the gift for personal greed and gain.

_ The Holy Spirit distributes the gift according to His will.

_ The church is a body and its members maintain an unbreakable and living relationships.

_ The church is institutional insofar as to maintain the order and better serve the body of the church.

9

Royal Priesthood

One of the greatest contributions of the Reformation was declaring the priesthood of all believers. Considering laymen as a royal priesthood is a fundamental truth that distinguishes Christianity from Catholicism.

But many Christians tend to forgot this glorious identity. There are some Christian communities that falsely teach that only the ministers have this right of priesthood.

This false teaching brings great harm to the body Christ of because it underestimates the potential of a believer. We must not forget and sell off our true identity with a bowl of soup as Esau did but rather be reminded that indeed, "I am a royal priesthood!"

Note

1. What can we learn from the following verses? Discuss the signifficance of the fact that these verses are from Isaiah and Revelation.

- Isaiah 61:6

Christians will be called priests of the Lord, ministers of God

- Revelation 1:6; 20:6

God made us to be a kingdom and priests. Second death doesn't have power over Gods ppl, they will reign with Christ for a 1000 yrs.

2. Compare the difference between the Old and New Testament regarding the High Priest and priesthood.

1) Who became the High Priest in the Old Testament? (Hebrews 5:1)

Those selected became high priest.

Note

2) Who is the High Priest in the New Testament Church? (Hebrews 4:14; 5:5; 9:11; 10:21)

Jesus Christ.

3) What is the fundamental difference between Jesus Christ and the human High Priest? (Hebrews 7:23~27)

Human high priests died. They had to continually sacrifice offerings for themselves and the ppl. Jesus lives eternally. He did die but was resurrected. The sacrifice he made was once and for all.

4) Who were the priests in the Old Testament? (Leviticus 21:1)

Sons of Aaron

Note

5) In the New Testament, all the saints are considered royal priesthood. What else is mentioned in 1 Peter 2:9?

A chosen ppl.
Royal priesthood
Holy nation
a ppl belonging to God, who were called out of darkness and into his marvelous light

3. We, as royal priesthood, have direct access to God. This is a wonderful privilege.

1) What does it mean to have a direct access to God? (Hebrews 10:19~22)

We can confidently enter the Most Holy Place through Christ

2) What are the benefits of this privilege?

- Romans 8:15

We received Spirit of sonship.
We are God's children.

Note

- Hebrews 4:16

we approach God w/ confidence
we may receive mercy and
find grace to help us in
our time of need

- John 16:23

God will give us whatever
we ask in God's name.

- 1 John 1:9

If we sin, He is faithful
and just and will forgive
our sins.

3) Share how this privilege can enhance your Christian life.

Confidence / security
in knowing my identity
Also confidence when
evangelizing. Joy that
God adopting me into
his family.

Note

4. As royal priesthood, we are able to offer spiritual sacrifices to God.

1) What is spiritual sacrifice? (Romans 12:1)

offering our bodies as a living sacrifice.

2) Here are a few examples of spiritual sacrifices.

- Hebrews 13:15

offering a sacrifice of praise fruit of lips that confess His name.

- Hebrews 13:16

do good and share w/ others

- Revelation 8:3

praying

- Psalm 116:17

we are God's servants.

Note

3) How are you convinced that your daily life at home and at work is an act of spiritual sacrifice to God?

My life is not my own, my life at home and work is His.

4) How does your life view change when you realize that your entire life is a living sacrifice to God?

I want to live it to bring glory to His name.

5. We are able to proclaim the Word of God.

1) How can witnessing be a sacrifice?

- Romans 15:16

they might become an Offering acceptable to God.

- 2 Corinthians 5:18, 19

proclaim the truth and so reconcile the world to Christ.

Note

- 1 Peter 2:9

declare God's praises; what He's done

2) How proud are you to be a witness?

Very!

6. We are able to intercede.

1) How many people are you interceding through your prayer? (1 Timothy 2:1~2)

everyone

2) Gal 6:2 mentions about carrying each other's burdens. How can this be related to intercessory prayer?

Crying out to God on behalf of brothers and sisters is intercessory prayer and carrying their burden.

Note

7. What have you learned from this chapter on Royal Priesthood?

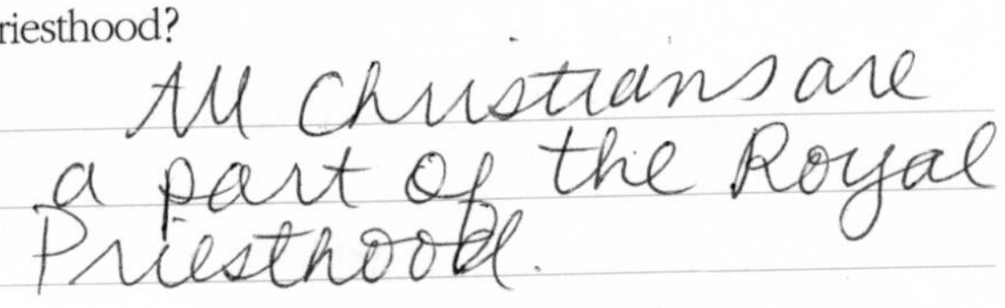

Doctrinal Summary

_ All Christians are priests.

_ There is no special status or class of priesthood in the church.

_ Jesus Christ is our only intercessor.

_ Church will be renewed when each member acts upon their true identity and role as royal priesthood.

Appendix

Bible Reading Guide

Bible Memory Verses

Self Check Chart

Bible Reading Guide

week	period	Training		day 1	day 2	day 3	day 4	day 5	day 6	day 7
		Discipleship	Ministry							
1	semester I	Orientation		Gen 1~2	3~5	6~9	10~11	12~14	15~17	18~20
2		1-1	1-1	21~24	25~26	27~31	32~36	37~40	41~44	45~47
3		1-2	1-2	48~50	Mt 1~4	5~7	8~11	12~15	16~19	20~23
4		1-3	1-3	24~25	26~28	Ex 1~2	3~6	7~10	11~12	13~15
5		1-4	1-4	16~18	19~20	21~24	25~27	28~31	32~34	35~40
6		1-5	1-5	Mk 1~3	4~7	8~10	11~13	14~16	Lev 1~3	4~7
7		1-6	1-6	8~10	11~15	16~17	18~20	21~23	24~27	Lk 1~2
8		2-1	2-1	3~6	7~9	10~12	13~15	16~18	19~21	22~24
9		2-2	2-2	Nu 1~4	5~8	9~12	13~16	17~20	21~25	26~30
10		2-3	2-3	31~33	34~36	Jn 1~2	3~5	6~8	9~12	13~17
11		2-4	2-4	18~21	Dt 1~4	5~7	8~11	12~16	17~20	21~26
12		2-5	2-5	27~30	31~34	Jos 1~5	6~8	9~12	13~17	18~21
13		2-6	2-6	22~24	Jag 1~5	6~8	9~12	13~16	17~21	Ru 1~4
14		2-7	2-7	Ac 1~4	5~7	8~9	10~12	13~15	16~18	19~20
15		2-8	2-8	21~23	24~26	27~28	1Sa 1~3	4~8	9~12	13~15
16		2-9	2-9	16~19	20~23	24~26	27~31	2Sa 1~4	5~7	8~10
17		2-10	3-1	11~14	15~18	19~20	21~24	Ro 1~3	4~5	6~8
18		2-11	3-2	9~11	12~16	1Ki 1~4	5~8	9~11	12~16	17~19
19		2-12	3-3	20~23	2Ki 1~3	4~8	9~12	13~17	18~21	22~25
20		2-13	3-4	1Ch 1~9	10~16	17~21	22~27	28~29	2Ch 1~5	6~9
21		2-14	3-5	10~12	13~16	17~20	21~25	26~28	29~32	33~36
22	vacation (Vac)	Vac-1	Vac-1	1Co 1~6	7~10	11~14	15~16	Ezr 1~3	4~6	Ezr 7~10 2Co 1~9
23		Vac-2	Vac-2	2Co 10~13	Ne 1~2	3~4	5~7	8~10	Ne 11~13	Gal 1~6 Est 1~7
24		Vac-3	Vac-3	Est 8~10	Job 1~3	4~7	8~10	11~14	15~17	Job 18~28
25		Vac-4	Vac-4	Job 29~31	32~34	35~37	38~39	40~42	Ps 1~6	Ps 7~30
26		Vac-5	Vac-5	Ps 31~36	37~41	42~49	50~54	55~59	60~66	67~89
27		Vac-6	Vac-6	Ps 90~97	98~103	104~106	107~110	111~118	119	Ps 120~145
28		Vac-7	Vac-7	Ps 146~150	Pr 1~4	5~9	10~13	14~17	18~21	Pr 22~31 Ecc 1~6
29		Vac-8	Vac-8	Ecc 7~12	Ss 1~8	Eph 1~6	Isa 1~4	5~7	8~12	13~20
30		Vac-9	Vac-9	Isa 21~23	24~27	28~30	31~35	36~39	40~43	44~48
31	semester II	3-1	3-6	Isa 49~51	52~57	58~62	63~66	Php 1~4	Jer 1~3	4~6
32		3-2	3-7	7~10	11~15	16~20	21~25	26~29	30~33	34~39
33		3-3	3-8	40~45	46~49	50~52	Col 1~4	La 1~5	1Th 1~5	Eze 1~6
34		3-4	3-9	7~11	12~15	16~19	20~23	24~28	29~32	33~36
35		3-5	4-1	37~39	40~43	44~48	2Th 1~3	Da 1~3	4~6	7~12
36		3-6	4-2	1Ti 1~6	Hos 1~3	4~6	7~8	9~11	12~14	2Ti 1~4
37		3-7	4-3	Joe 1~3	Tit 1~3	Am 1~2	3~5	6~7	8~9	Phm
38		3-8	4-4	Ob	Heb 1~2	3~4	5~7	8~10	11~13	Jnh 1~4
39		3-9	4-5	Jas 1~5	Mic 1~2	3~5	6~7	1Pe 1~5	Na 1~3	2Pe 1~3
40		3-10	4-6	Hab 1~3	1Jn 1~5	Zep 1~3	2Jn	Hag 1~2	3Jn	Zec 1~2
41		3-11	Lecture I	3~4	5~6	7~8	9~11	12~14	Jude	Mal 1~4
42		3-12	Lecture II	Rev 1~3	4~6	7~9	10~13	14~16	17~19	20~22

Bible Memory Verses

Theme	Wk.	Title	Scripture	
Key to New Life: Holy Spirit	1	No More Condemnation	Rom 8:1~4	
	2	Spiritually Minded Person	Rom 8:5~11	
	3	Dying to the Flesh	Rom 8:12~16	
	4	Heirs to the Suffering and Glory	Rom 8:17~25	
	5	Two Promises	Rom 8:26~30	
	6	Unbreakable Relationship	Rom 8:31~39	
Church and Laity	7	What is Church?	Eph 2:19~20	Review 1 ✓
	8	Existence of Church: Worship	Jn 4:23~24	Review 2 ✓
	9	Existence of Church: Training	Eph 4:11~13	Review 3 ✓
	10	Existence of Church: Witnessing	1Pe 2:11~12	Evaluation 1~3 ✓
	11	Qualification of a Disciple: Total Dependence	Lk 14:26~27, 33	Review 4 ✓
	12	Qualification of a Disciple: Witness	Lk 24:46~48	Review 5 ✓
	13	Qualification of a Disciple: Servant	1Co 4:5	Review 6
	14	Members of the Body and the Cooperative Ministry	Col 3:16~17	Evaluation 4~6
	15	Royal Priesthood	1Pe 2:9	Review 1
Small Group and Leadership	16	Learning Environment of Small Group Bible Study	Heb 10:24~45	Review 2
	17	Small Group Bible Study and Leadership	1Th 2:7~8	Review 3
	18	How to Lead a Small Group Bible Study	Ps 1:1~2	Evaluation 1~3
	19	Inductive Bible Study Practice (1): Observation	Isa 34:16	Review 4
	20	Inductive Bible Study Practice (2): Interpretation	Jas 1:5	Review 5
	21	Inductive Bible Study Practice (3): Application	Heb 3:13	Review 6
	22	Leading Inductive Bible Study	1Ti 4:12	Evaluation 4~6
	23	Internship and Evaluation	Heb 13:7	Evaluation 1~6
	24	Practice and Evaluation	2Ti 2:2	Evaluation 1~6

Self Check Chart

Name

Check by symbols ○ : All completed △: Partially completed ×: Incomplete

Date	Subject Matter	Preparation	QT	Memory Verse	Bible Reading	Special Project	Leader (Check the Work)